CW00393558

ISBN 978-2-211-06708-9

Loi numéro 49 956 du 16 juillet 1949 sur les publications
destinées à la jeunesse : septembre 2002
Dépôt légal : juillet 2007
Imprimé en France par Aubin Imprimeur à Poitiers

Stephanie Blake

Caca boudin

l'école des loisirs
11, rue de Sèvres, Paris 6e

Il
était
une
fois
un lapin qui
ne savait dire
qu'UNE
chose...

Caca boudin

Le matin,
sa maman
lui disait :
« Debout,
mon petit lapin ! »
Il répondait :

Caca boudin

Le midi,
son papa
lui disait :
« Mange tes épinards,
mon petit lapin ! »
Il répondait :

Caca
boudin

Le soir,
sa grande sœur
lui disait :
« Viens prendre ton bain,
mon petit lapin ! »
Il répondait :

Caca boudin

Un jour,
un loup
lui dit :
« Je peux te manger,
mon petit lapin ? »
Il répondit :

Caca
boudin

Alors,
le loup
mangea
le petit lapin.

Lorsque le loup
rentra
chez lui,
sa femme lui dit :
« Ça va, mon chéri ? »
Le loup répondit :

Caca boudin

Quelques
heures
plus tard,
le loup
ne se sentait
pas bien…
Il appela
le médecin.

Le médecin dit :
« Faites aah... »
Le loup répondit :
« Caca boudin ! »
Alors, le médecin
s'exclama :
« Mais !
vous avez mangé
mon petit lapin ! »

Le médecin
qui n'avait peur de
rien
alla chercher
son
petit
lapin.

Lorsque le papa lapin
retrouva son petit, il dit :
« Ah ! mon petit
Caca boudin ! »
Le petit lapin, fort surpris,
s'exclama :
« Mais enfin, cher père,
comment osez-vous
m'appeler ainsi ?
Je m'appelle

Simon,

vous le savez bien ! »

De retour à la maison,
sa maman lui dit :
« Mange ta soupe,
mon petit lapin ! »
Il répondit :
« Oh oui ! comme c'est exquis ! »
Mais le lendemain matin,
lorsque son papa lui dit :
« Brosse tes dents,
mon petit lapin »,
il répondit :

Prout !

Written by Amy Wilson

Edited by Philippa Wingate
Designed by Button plc
Produced by Joanne Rooke

Picture Credits

David Fisher/Rex Features: front cover, pages 21 and 36
Ken McKay/Rex Features: back cover, endpapers, pages 6, 8-9, 12, 15, 16-17, 18, 23, 42-43, 45, 51, 54-55, 57 and 59
Mark Campbell/Rex Features: pages 25, 30, 41 and 52
Stuart Atkins/Rex Features: page 11
Huw John/Rex Features: pages 47 and 60
Rex Features: pages 33 and 35

First published in Great Britain in 2006 by Buster Books,
an imprint of Michael O'Mara Books Limited,
16 Lion Yard, Tremadoc Road, London SW4 7NQ

A CIP catalogue record for this book is available from the British Library.

ISBN – 10 digit: 1–905158–46–7
ISBN – 13 digit: 978–1–905158–46–1

10 9 8 7 6 5 4 3 2 1

Printed and bound in Italy by L.E.G.O.

Shayne Ward

Shayne Ward
UNAUTHORISED
ANNUAL 2007

Contents

W

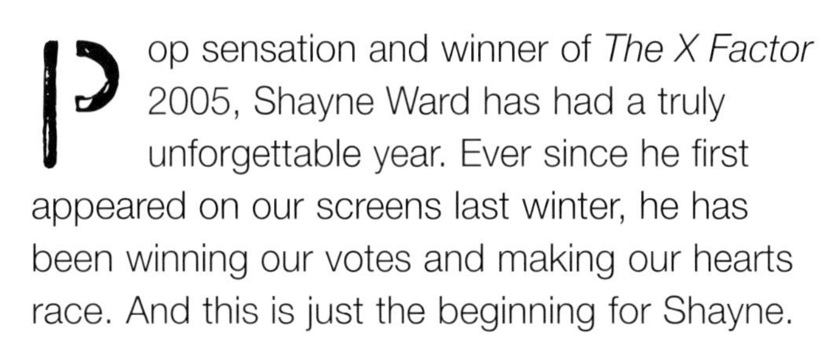

Introducing Shayne Ward

Pop sensation and winner of *The X Factor* 2005, Shayne Ward has had a truly unforgettable year. Ever since he first appeared on our screens last winter, he has been winning our votes and making our hearts race. And this is just the beginning for Shayne.

The former shop assistant from Manchester won huge public support as he stormed through round after round of *The X Factor*, charming the tough panel of judges. The moment when Shayne became the show's second winner will not be forgotten by the millions of viewers who voted for him.

And for Shayne, life will never be the same. Still only in his early twenties, he has now toured the country, attracted hordes of fans who watch his every move, and partied hard with some of the world's best-known celebrities. What's more, Shayne has become the darling of the music industry, with a Christmas number one and a debut album that has been a runaway success.

In this book you'll find out everything you want to know about Britain's brightest new star – his thoughts on fame, money, love and family. You might even find out a few things that he'd rather you didn't know. There are flow charts to follow, a quiz to fill in that will test your fan credentials, and loads of gorgeous photos of Shayne that are guaranteed to make you swoon. So don't tease yourself any longer, read on and receive your 're-Ward'.

Fact File

Name:
Shayne Thomas Ward

Date Of Birth:
16th October 1984

Eyes:
Blue

Hair:
Brown

Height:
5 feet and 9 inches

Star Sign:
Libra

Birthplace:
Hattersley, Tameside, Greater Manchester

Lives:
Manchester

School:
St. Peter's R.C. High School, Manchester

Favourite Subject At School:
Performing Arts

Previous Occupation:
Working in New Look, Arndale Centre, Manchester

The Early Years

Here's a brief history of Shayne's life before fame came calling. From the very beginning he showed star quality...

Family Man

Shayne was born in Hattersley in Tameside, Greater Manchester, in 1984. He is the youngest son of a large family, with three older brothers, Mark, Martin and Michael, and three sisters: older sister Lisa, his twin Emma, and the baby of the family, Leona.

A Fighter

Shayne may seem to have led a charmed life, but it hasn't always been that way. Born two months prematurely, doctors gave him only 24 hours to live because he couldn't breathe properly. But Shayne has always been a fighter, and by the time he was just four years old he was entertaining his family with some very powerful lungs indeed.

Passionate

Singing has always been Shayne's greatest passion. He and sister Emma used to sing Kylie Minogue's classic 'I Should Be So Lucky' together. His second love is dancing. He's self-taught, and believes that he can hold his own on most dance floors. "I was always the first to start singing and performing; I just couldn't help myself," Shayne confesses.

School Days

Elizabeth Kennedy, who taught Shayne when he was ten years old, realised he had real promise from the start. "I always knew Shayne would make it, one way or another," she says.

Young Shayne loved the stage, even while at school. He was cast as the romantic lead in several school productions. He once played Elvis Presley and was Tony in a St. Peter's production of *West Side Story*.

Moving On

After school, Shayne went on to work as a shop assistant at New Look in Manchester's Arndale Centre – but he didn't give up on his dreams of performing. He was a member of a band called Destiny. "It was great being in the band," he says. "A lot of hard work, but we were enjoying ourselves and doing pretty well."

Keen Contestant

Shayne has always been a very determined lad. He began entering television talent shows as a teenager, and won his way through to be one of the final thirty contestants in TV's *Pop Idol* competition. He also appeared in *Popstars: The Rivals*.

Unsurprisingly, Shayne is a big fan of talent contests. "I think they're brilliant because, more than anything, people who are trying to get record deals just try their hardest for so long. They try everything, for years, and still get nowhere. Then these competitions come up and give the people at home the chance to decide whether they like the singers or not. So it's not just one person or a few people at a record company deciding who gets a chance to go out there and prove what they can do. It puts it to the test. I think they're brilliant."

And it was as a result of just such a television talent show, *The X Factor*, that Shayne himself got the chance to show people just what he could do.

The X Factor

From the moment Shayne first appeared on *The X Factor* it was clear he was a real contender. Here's the story of his progress through the top TV talent contest.

First Hurdles

Shayne romped through the early rounds of the competition, encouraged by positive feedback from all three judges – Simon Cowell, Louis Walsh and Sharon Osbourne. "You are the one to watch in this competition. I can see you in this competition until the very, very end," commented Simon Cowell, who is notoriously difficult to please.

In return, Shayne has kind words to say about Simon. "Simon Cowell is not Mr Nasty. He speaks the truth and doesn't lie. He doesn't throw compliments at me to keep me happy. When he says 'well done', I know he really means it. He really loves good music," Shayne enthused.

Louis's Man

When Shayne received the news that Louis Walsh was to be his mentor, he was delighted. "Louis was definitely my first choice as a mentor. When the curtains went back at boot camp and I got Louis, I was over the moon," he confessed.

It wasn't long before Shayne was winning over the audience with his renditions of hits such as Justin Timberlake's 'Cry Me A River' and Take That's 'A Million Love Songs'.

Louis, on the other hand, wasn't finding the competition quite so easy. He sensationally quit at one point. But Shayne tried to keep positive, saying that his mentor would still be supporting him and giving him advice. Sure enough, when Louis returned to the programme, things were as good as new. "I never felt abandoned by him," Shayne said.

The Home Straight

Finally, after weeks of performing in front of the judges and the viewers at home, Shayne got through to the semi-finals. "People only dream of this. I've dreamt of it and it's actually coming true. I've achieved a lot more than I expected," he admitted. "I'm really happy to be in the semi-final. I never expected to get this far ... I would absolutely love it if I got to the final, I really would."

So what happened next? Just in case it has become a little blurry in all the excitement, here is a reminder – Shayne scooped a place in the final alongside Andy Abraham and the two brothers known as Journey South (all shown with Shayne on the next page). The stage was set for the final showdown.

itv1
itv

FACTOR

Simply The Best

Who won *The X Factor*? Do we really need to remind you? Weren't you sitting there, biting your nails, praying for victory for the young lad from Manchester?

Tense Times

It was an incredibly tense finale to the series – and not just for the fans! Shayne admits to being fairly anxious himself. He performed Daniel Bedingfield's 'If You're Not The One', Johnny Mathis's 'When A Child Is Born' and Judy Garland's 'Over The Rainbow'. "I was really nervous. I was thinking, 'All the performances I've done – that's nothing now. This is the one.' But when I got on the stage, the crowd were fantastic. They build you up," Shayne remembers.

The Votes Are Counted

In the end it was a close call. Nearly 11 million people voted. When the finalists stood on stage to hear the results, the tension was heart-stopping. Then came the announcement – Journey South were out of the running.

Finally, Andy and Shayne took to the stage to sing their versions of the single 'That's My Goal', written specially for *The X Factor* winner. Then all they could do was wait to hear who had won. Shayne admits, "I was the most nervous I've ever been. I've never wanted something so much in my life and I wasn't expecting my name to be read out to be honest."

Tears of a Winner

The winner of *The X Factor* 2005 is ... Shayne" were the words the nation had waited to hear. Shayne promptly burst into tears and hugged fellow competitor Andy. It had been very close. Shayne beat his rival by only 1.5 per cent of the vote.

After the show, the star just couldn't stop thanking his fans. "I want to say a big thank you to everybody that voted for me. You've made me and my family the happiest people in the world and I owe you everything. I just hope I can give back now what you've given to me. Thank you so much," he said. "I've never wanted anything more in my life."

Shayne On The Competition

During the *X Factor* tour, Shayne found himself back with his fellow contestants. Here are some of the things he has said about the people he beat on his way to the top.

Shayne On Chico

"I think it is fantastic that it isn't just me who got something from the show. I think Chico is a great performer. He has been very honest and admitted he is not the best singer in the world, but he makes up for that with his dancing and his personality ... I was delighted that Chico got his number one."

Check out the picture opposite of Chico offering a helping hand when Shayne fell on the ice. Ouch!

Shayne On Journey South

The duo have done pretty well since they lost out to Shayne. They joined forces with Simon Cowell and released their debut album. Shayne says he is delighted for them.

Shayne On Andy Abraham

Since finishing second in the final in December, the forty-one-year-old from Acton, London, has signed a deal with Sony and released his debut album called *The Impossible Dream*.

Shayne was sure Andy would beat him in *The X Factor* competition, and said afterwards, "I wish all the best to him. He's a great guy and he deserves it."

Shayne On The Competition

Shayne On Steve Brookstein

The first winner of *The X Factor* has not enjoyed the same success as Shayne, and has even been known to criticise the show. But Shayne is not letting that dampen his spirits. "Obviously there is a lot of feeling out there – like, 'Is Shayne Ward going to be another talent-show flop?' And if I am, then I am. If it happens, it happens. But if I do not stick around then I know I will not slate the show." Shayne a flop? We can't imagine it.

On The Rest ...

Of course, Shayne isn't just competing against *The X Factor* contestants now – he's up there with the best music stars around. He has already had a showdown for the UK number-one spot with NizLopi, among others, but Shayne emerged the winner.

Now Shayne wants people to start taking a fresh look at the pop world. He's on a bit of a crusade, and we're sure others will join him. "I think that people are losing interest too easily in some of the songs that are coming out," says Shayne.

And as for Shayne's own taste in music? "I listen to every type of music," he says. "Everyone that's out in the charts now and back in the day – the 60s, 70s, 80s, 90s and now. I look up to them because they've done what I'm about to do now."

And his favourite band? That would be Keane. "I've been listening a lot to Keane's *Hopes and Fears*. I really love that album," reveals Shayne.

JIMI HENDRIX
JUSTIN HAWKINS

Shayne Fever

Winning *The X-Factor* would be a dream for most people, and of course, for Shayne, it was a dream come true. Life since the competition has been a rollercoaster. As soon as our hunk was named champion, the music world became Shayne's playground.

Debut Single

Record stores ordered 750,000 advance copies of his debut single, 'That's My Goal', and it just flew off the shelves. It scooped the Christmas number-one spot and became the second highest-selling single of 2005, with more than 300,000 copies sold on the first day alone.

Shayne's success even earned him a place in *The Guinness Book of Records*. 'That's My Goal' was the best-selling download in UK history, with 46,000 copies downloaded in just four days. But, true to form, Shayne didn't let it go to his head. "It's not all about the money and the fame. I entered *The X Factor* because I love singing. I was doing working men's clubs and pubs before and I loved that. But this is a dream."

And things could get even better. Shayne's mentor Louis Walsh has said, "Shayne has the potential to be [the next] Robbie Williams or Will Young."

Second Release

As he prepared to launch his second single, 'No Promises', Shayne began a whirlwind promotional tour. The record landed at the number-two spot – no mean achievement for a star who was unheard of until just over a year ago!

Album Launch

In April 2006, Shayne launched his first solo album with an event in Manchester's Albert Square. A massive 15,000 fans, including his friends and family, turned up to wish him well. Shayne performed a six-song set, which included 'Over The Rainbow'.

The album, called simply *Shayne Ward*, shot to the top of the UK charts, selling a record 201,000 copies in one week alone.

Despite the countrywide outbreak of severe Shayne fever, our boy is keeping his cool as he looks towards the future.

SALE
70%
£9.99
SALE
£9.99

Timeline

This has been the best year of Shayne's life – one to remember. Here's a timeline of some of his top moments.

2005

15th October: A very nervous Shayne sings Bryan Adams's 'Right Here Waiting For You', his first live performance on *The X Factor*.

22nd October: Shayne continues to impress with Daniel Bedingfield's 'If You're Not The One'

29th October: Shayne ups the ante with Bryan Adams' 'Summer Of '69'.

5th November: Our favourite lad wins more hearts with 'You Make Me Feel Brand New'.

12th November: Shayne dazzles with a performance of Justin Timberlake's 'Cry Me A River'.

19th November: Shayne performs the Take That classic 'A Million Love Songs'.

26th November: The star makes The Darkness's 'I Believe In A Thing Called Love' his own.

3rd December: Shayne wows the crowds with George Michael's 'Careless Whisper' and Scissor Sisters' 'Take Your Mama Out'.

10th December: The crooner belts out Queen's 'Don't Stop Me Now' and the Righteous Brothers' classic 'Unchained Melody'.

17th December: The all–important final performances of Daniel Bedingfield's 'If You're Not The One', Johnny Mathis's 'When A Child Is Born', Judy Garland's 'Over The Rainbow' and 'That's My Goal' win the day.

21st December: 'That's My Goal' is released and becomes an instant hit and Christmas number one.

25th December: Shayne appears on the Christmas *Top of the Pops.*

2006

10th January: 'That's My Goal' is nominated for a BRIT Award in the Best Single category.

16th February: *The X Factor* performers go on tour to Newcastle.

18th February: The tour hits in Glasgow.

26th February: *The X Factor* tour goes to London.

6th March: Cardiff gets *The X Factor* treatment.

3rd March: Shayne makes a triumphant return to his home town when *The X Factor* tour reaches Manchester.

10th March: Birmingham is won over by *The X Factor* tour.

10th April: Shayne's second single 'No Promises' is released.

17th April: *Shayne Ward,* the album, is released.

And still to come ...

... Shayne's solo tour will take place in February 2007, with dates already lined up in Glasgow, Newcastle, Manchester, Sheffield and Wembley. A tour of Ireland is also on the cards.

An A To Z Of Shayne

As one of Shayne's top fans, you probably think you know all there is to know about our favourite crooner. But sometimes even the best can miss a few things – so here is an A to Z of Mr Ward to help you brush up.

A is for ALBUM. *Shayne Ward*, the album, flew off the shelves the moment it hit the shops and proved that Shayne is a major talent.

B is for BLING. Gucci suits and diamond earrings are just par for the course when one is a hot celebrity – and Shayne has no problem with that! Well, he wouldn't, would he?

C is for CALVIN KLEIN. Rumour has it that Shayne is following in the footsteps of Kate Moss and doing press and TV ads for fashion designer Calvin Klein. Yummy!

D is for DREAMS. Shayne has seen all his dreams come true since winning *The X Factor*.

E is for EMMA. Shayne and his twin sister Emma have been entertaining the rest of their family since they were small, and they celebrated their birthday together during *The X Factor* competition with a special cake.

F is for FOOTBALL. Shayne is passionate about football and will start to drool if you mention Manchester United.

G is for GIRLS. Shayne has had plenty of attention from the fairer sex since he first got up on stage, but the star takes it all in his stride, with a little help from his minder ...

H is for HOLLYWOOD. Shayne isn't ruling out Tinsel Town. He says he'd love to be in a film one day. We're sure we'd love that, too.

I is for IPOD. Shayne just wouldn't be without his iPod.

J is for JOKER. The hunk has a naughty streak – literally! He once streaked across a cricket pitch wearing a bright pink wig and little else.

K is for KENNEDY. Shayne's teacher, Elizabeth Kennedy, saw his star potential from the start.

L is for LINKIN PARK. This band has Shayne's vote.

M is for MANCHESTER. Shayne is very loyal to his home city and has a massive fan base there.

N is for 'NO PROMISES'. Shayne's second single swooped into the number-two spot and proved the star to be much more than a one-hit wonder.

O is for OPEN-TOP. The pink Cadillac in which Shayne toured Manchester will never be forgotten.

P is for PAMPERING. Shayne is all in favour of a little TLC! He regularly uses moisturiser, though he says he would draw the line at having his eyebrows plucked.

Q is for QUEEN. Shayne was helped to victory with his performance of the Queen song 'Don't Stop Me Now'.

R is for ROCK. Shayne's not a big fan of heavy rock and metal music.

S is for SEEING DOUBLE. Just days after Shayne won the top spot on *The X Factor*, he had his own lookalike, Paul Cole. Business is brisk and it looks like Paul might have found himself a long-term career.

T is for TUSSAUDS (as in Madame Tussauds). Shayne hadn't been in the limelight for a year before he got his own looky-likey model in the VIP Blush room at the famous London tourist venue.

U is for USA. Shayne has already made his mark on the States. Simon Cowell presented the star at a Sony event stateside and, true to form, Shayne won everybody's hearts – so watch this space!

V is for VOCAL CORDS. These babies are pretty important to a singer. Shayne strained his vocal cords just before the *X Factor* tour but battled on regardless – our hero!

W is for WOOLWORTHS. One of Shayne's first jobs as a celebrity was to appear in a Woolworths advertisement.

X is for *THE X FACTOR*. Shayne will never forget the TV programme that propelled him into the limelight and gave the country a real star.

Y is for 'YOU MAKE ME FEEL BRAND NEW'. Who can forget Shayne's rendition of this classic song?

Z is for ZZZ. Shayne just doesn't get enough sleep these days, what with his super celebrity lifestyle. Poor Mr Ward!

Shayn

Ward-search

d	r	a	w	e	n	y	a	h	s
w	i	n	n	e	r	s	h	h	d
h	p	u	d	m	m	a	a	e	u
i	o	g	e	m	g	r	f	n	a
s	d	o	n	a	o	h	o	i	s
p	w	a	y	n	d	f	h	v	s
e	i	l	i	s	a	v	w	e	u
r	p	r	o	t	c	a	f	x	t
k	r	a	p	n	i	k	n	i	l
c	p	r	o	m	i	s	e	s	c

Can you find the following words in the grid above? You'll find the answers on page 58.

ipod
sharon
linkin park
promises
x factor
winner
shayne ward
emma
whisper
goal
tussauds

What Shayne Said

Ever since he scooped the *X Factor* crown, Shayne has been in the limelight. The modest star has taken it all in his stride, though. Here are a few things he has said since he became our number-one guy.

Shayne On Winning *The X Factor*: "You have made my dream come true – I am still in shock. I am completely overwhelmed."

Shayne On His Christmas Number One: "I am so thrilled to top the charts at Christmas. Thank you to everyone who bought 'That's My Goal' and all the thousands of people who voted for me on *The X Factor*."

Shayne On Being In *The Guinness Book Of Records*: "I'm only twenty-one and I'm in *The Guinness Book of Records*. How amazing is that?"

Shayne On His Celebrity Lifestyle: "I'm just somewhere up in the clouds right now. I've met so many amazing people. I've had a good talk with Robbie Williams. He found out where I was and said: 'I'd like to meet him,' so he came in and gave me a big hug and said he supported me and had voted for me. It was unbelievable."

Shayne On the *X Factor* Tour: "It's great to see the guys again and the fans are the best."

Shayne On The Parties: "The BRIT Awards were very cool and I went to the after party for that, and I went to a great party in Miami – Leonardo DiCaprio was there!"

Shayne On His Favourite Track On The Album: "I'm really pleased with how the album has turned out and I can't pick a favourite. There is the version of 'Over The Rainbow' I did for *The X Factor* final – which is one of my favourites as it was such an emotional night."

Shayne On His Family: "We are very close and never let anything come between us."

"My hero is definitely my mum – she's always my number one."

Shayne On The Music Scene: "I do believe that pop is coming back now. I think that it's a good thing, that's what we need right now. We need the charts to be full of it."

What The Media Said

When you're as famous as Shayne Ward, you become a bit of a media magnet – just going shopping is enough to attract attention from the paparazzi. Winning over the media is important for Shayne, particularly as they're the ones who will be reviewing his albums and videos. So far Shayne has made a good start. Read on ...

The Guardian: "On paper, Ward is a dream rags-to-riches star. When good looks and talent came together on television, they allowed him a glimpse of a new future."

The Observer: "He is about as raw and unmediated as any pop star arriving in the public realm can be right now."

New Woman magazine: "The sexiest thing ever to come out of reality TV." The magazine ran a poll to find the world's sexiest man, and Shayne scooped number seven! Brad Pitt claimed the top spot, but Shayne beat off competition from Robbie Williams, who came thirteenth.

The Sun: "Undoubtedly one of the hottest young talents in the UK today."

Now magazine: "Whether he wins or loses, there's no question that Shayne has a future. His mentor Louis Walsh has already offered to manage his career, and with a huge teen following (he's the cover boy on a host of mags), he could turn out to be the break-out star of the year."

Heat magazine: "Not since Justin Timberlake has there been a male singer who's inspired such feelings of lust in women across the country. Grannies, teenage girls, happily married women – they all love him."

AWARDS
Pioneer

Shayne On Love

With his swoonsome good looks and an easygoing nature, Shayne is a natural hottie. Add to that a hefty dash of celebrity glamour and ... yummy! But what does Shayne have to say about love and the women in his life?

Ideal Girlfriend: Shayne's honey would have to be very honest and have a nice personality – she would also need to take a real pride in her appearance. Not so keen on the old jeans and T-shirt look, are we Shayne? He loves girls who would treat him well – rustling up a cheese flan or a meat-and-potato pie would get you straight into his good books.

Star Girl: Our blue-eyed boy is certainly particular about who he would like to be seen with. Even international beauties like Angelina Jolie aren't quite up to scratch, he just doesn't see the attraction.

Ideal Date: He once wooed a girl by filling a hotel room with chocolates, champagne, flowers and candles, and writing a poem. What a sweetie.

Fabulous Fans: "It's nice to get some attention from the girls, but, so far, they have been kept away from me," he says. "Apparently I get lots of mail but I don't get to see it, which is annoying. It is all screened."

Love Confessions: "I was very shy. At school I only ever had two girlfriends," admits Shayne. We bet they were the envy of the whole school! Even when he was old enough to go partying, Shayne wasn't a ladies' man. "When I used to go out clubbing, I always thought girls wouldn't look at me in any fanciable way. I've never approached a girl in my life."

Mother Love: Shayne asks his mum for tips on how to win girls' hearts. Any girl who wanted to get close to Shayne would have to be extra nice to Mrs Ward.

Love Match?

Starting in the pink box at the top of page 39, answer the questions, go with the flow, and find out whether you are right for Shayne romantically or destined to be just good friends. You can follow only a pink arrow into a question box and a blue arrow out of it.

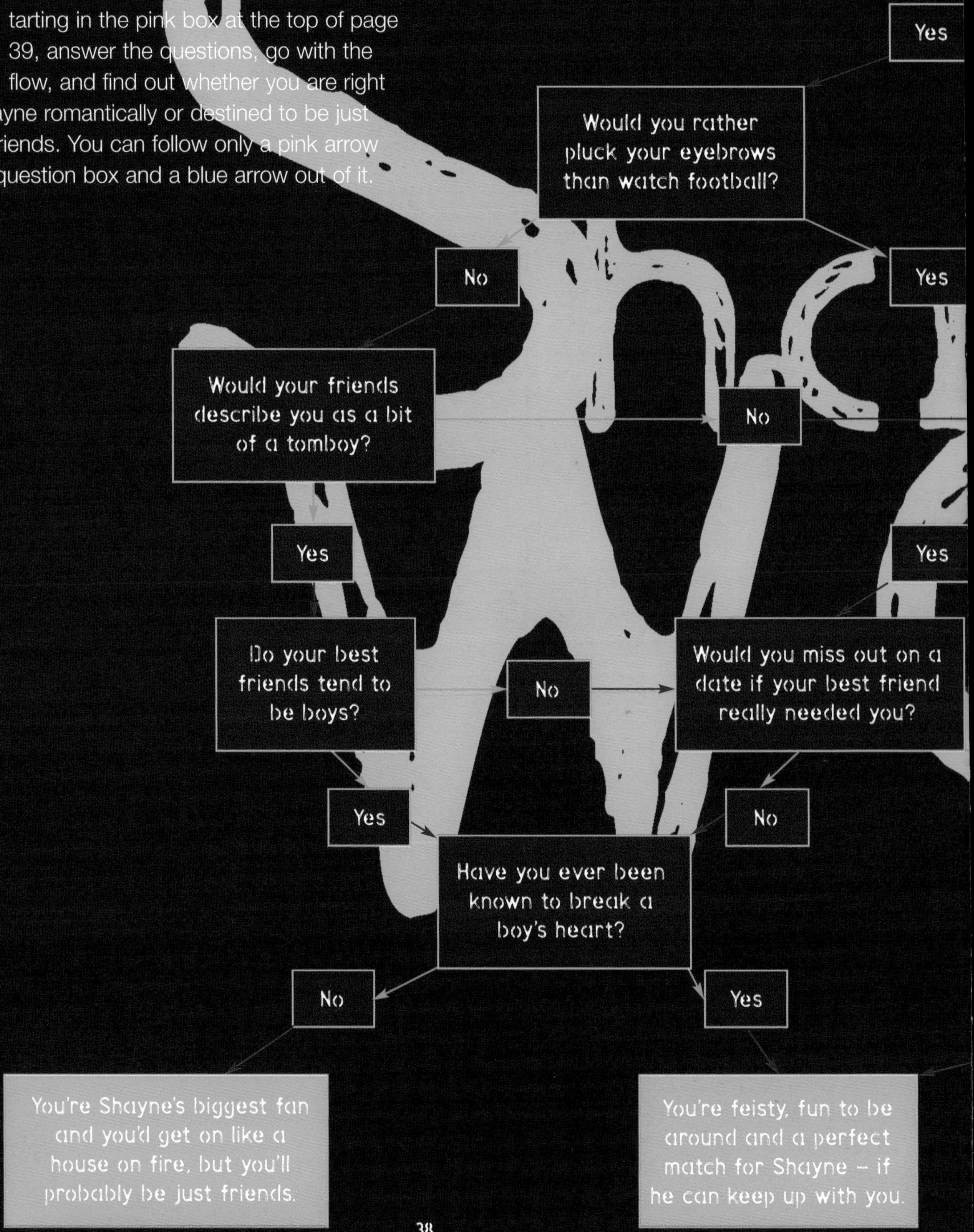

Yes

Would you rather pluck your eyebrows than watch football?

No

Yes

Would your friends describe you as a bit of a tomboy?

No

Yes

Yes

Do your best friends tend to be boys?

No

Would you miss out on a date if your best friend really needed you?

Yes

No

Have you ever been known to break a boy's heart?

No

Yes

You're Shayne's biggest fan and you'd get on like a house on fire, but you'll probably be just friends.

You're feisty, fun to be around and a perfect match for Shayne – if he can keep up with you.

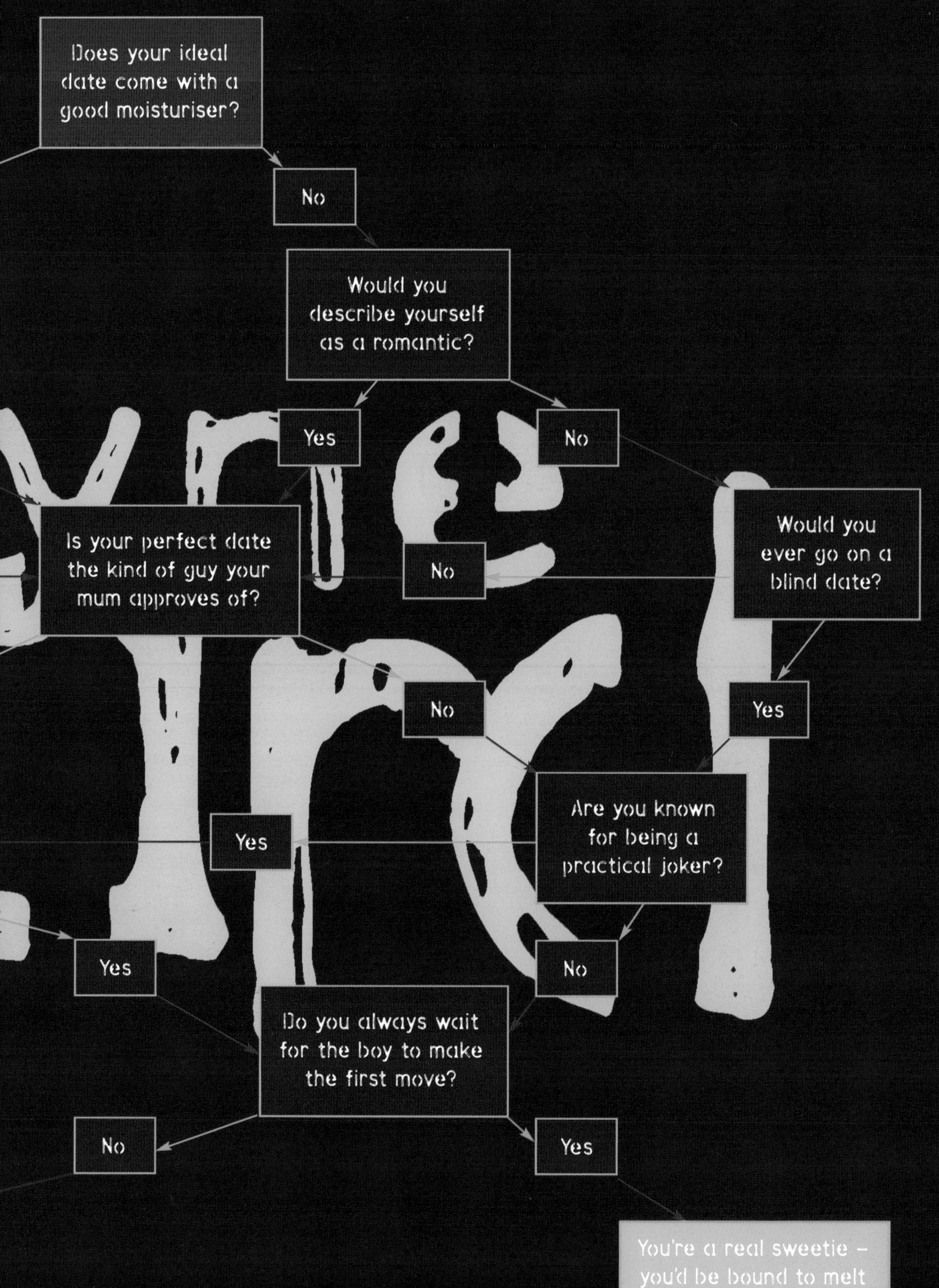

Does your ideal date come with a good moisturiser?
No
Would you describe yourself as a romantic?
Yes
No
Is your perfect date the kind of guy your mum approves of?
No
Would you ever go on a blind date?
No
Yes
Are you known for being a practical joker?
Yes
Yes
No
Do you always wait for the boy to make the first move?
No
Yes
You're a real sweetie – you'd be bound to melt Shayne's heart.

The Fame Factor

Overnight fame sounds pretty cool – who wouldn't want the jet-set lifestyle, the serious money, the adoring fans? But it takes time to learn how to deal with the media frenzy. How does Shayne cope with being in the spotlight 24/7?

Fabulous Factor

The fact that Shayne Ward is seriously gorgeous has not gone unnoticed. He is one of the most photographed hunks of the year. There isn't a week that goes by without some hot gossip about him appearing in print. But Shayne is too chuffed with his success to be bothered by a few cameras – they are a small price to pay for the glitz and glamour he enjoys. "It's the greatest feeling and it's just absolutely fantastic, but the fame hasn't hit me yet," he says.

Hard Work

Shayne admits: "It's all work, work, work, to be honest. I haven't really had time for anything else." But Shayne's not complaining. He waited a long time to make it big on the music scene, and he is going to make the most of it, no matter what. "I've been working with the best producers around. I'm having the time of my life."

Difficult Times

Of course, it isn't all plain sailing. Shayne's success has attracted a few jealous poison pen letters, but Shayne deals with them in his laid-back manner. "It's bound to happen," he shrugs. "Not everyone is going to like you. I just rise above it." Good for you, Shayne.

What does bother the star, occasionally, is being away from home a lot – what with the tours and the video shoots. His close-knit family have had to make do with brief phone calls and even briefer visits, and his friends are all missing him. But they need not worry – Shayne is a loyal lad who won't let fame change him.

Going Home

When he does go home, Shayne is instantly mobbed by his adoring fans. One of the first things he had to do after he won *The X Factor* was to hire a full-time minder to control the hordes of fans who surround him.

The humble hunk is still amazed by the attention. "I was asked to sing when the Christmas lights were turned on in the Trafford Centre. I got out of the car, and suddenly there were thousands of people screaming my name. I thought, 'Hang on, is this for me?' I loved it. I went into showbiz mode and started strutting about. But as soon as I was on my own, behind closed doors, I was like 'Phew. Did that really happen?'"

Keeping It Real

Shayne just wants to take his chance while he can. "I'm like a slave to the hard work! Photo shoots, interviews, signings. I'm having the time of my life, though," he says. "There's nothing about being famous that worries me. All I've got to do is sing; so that's my main focus. I'm not going to let anything get in my way. I've made it this far, so if I keep focused I'll be fine." We are sure you are right, Shayne!

Shh... Shayne's Secrets

Here is the low-down on a few things the star would rather keep close to his hunky chest. Don't worry, your secrets are safe with us, Shayne ... honest.

- Shayne may have got the hang of singing and charming the nation, but he just can't seem to get the hang of driving. One of the first things he spent money on after he won *The X Factor* was driving lessons.

- If nosy Shayne could make a wish, he'd like to be an invisible man and go around seeing what everyone else gets up to.

- Shayne has said that in a film about his life he would like to be played by Justin Timberlake.

- Looking cool is pretty easy for Shayne, but he has not always been so perfect. He once bought a £70 mullet wig that made him look like 80s television star Pat Sharp – not a good look!

- Shayne confesses that sometimes even he would like a bit of normality – a cup of tea at home with his mum, rather than partying with the likes of Robbie Williams.

- There are many posters and calendars of Shayne available, but he'd rather not see them, thanks very much. "I get embarrassed looking at pictures of myself," he admits. He reckons he looks flabby and he doesn't like the tattoos on his arms. We say, "No way!"

- Shayne has bought only one CD in his life, a copy of Daniel Bedingfield's 'If You're Not The One'.

- Shayne's family and friends all have to be patient with the star – no matter how much he loves them, it still takes Shayne three or four days to answer a text message!

- Shayne often receives fans' underwear, sent to him at home or thrown at him on stage! Guess it's par for the course when you're a dishy performer.

Shayne On Tour

No pop star's existence would be complete without a tour, and Shayne has certainly got to grips with travelling around the country singing his heart out. Touring is time-consuming and not always the glamorous existence one might imagine, but Shayne's having a ball all the same.

For The Fans

Shayne couldn't wait to get out on the road with the *X Factor* tour, which followed the hit show. "I've been itching to get on stage and perform live since the night I won *The X Factor*," he said. "This has always been my dream, and I would never want to miss the opportunity to perform to thousands of people who are fans of the show and who voted for me."

Home From Home

And there were no complaints once he started the tour. "I have so much fun travelling around. I get on really well with my tour manager, and because I'm so busy I don't get homesick. I don't really have time to think about home," said Shayne.

Highlights

The *X Factor* tour ran from 16th February to 15th March 2006, and also featured other contestants including Chico, Journey South and runner-up Andy Abraham.

The tour dates in Shayne's home city of Manchester were his favourites. At a gig at the Arndale Centre, Manchester, he performed to the same shoppers he used to serve before he hit the limelight. His three dates at the Manchester Evening News Arena saw him sing to an audience of more than 50,000 people. "I couldn't believe a boy from Clayton had made it on to that stage. Standing in front of so many fans was amazing. I get lots of boxers and thongs thrown at me," he enthused.

Health Fears

It hasn't all been easy for the blue-eyed idol. At one point it seemed he might not be able to take part in the *X Factor* tour because of throat problems. Tests revealed that Shayne had a nodule on his vocal cords, and there were fears he would be unable to appear alongside the show's other finalists. But, true to form, Shayne was determined to battle on. "I went to see a specialist and they told me that singers often suffer from this problem, and that it's nothing to worry about."

Going Solo

Shayne's next tour is already on the horizon – his first solo tour will hit the road in February 2007. "I can't imagine what it will be like to sing for so many people on my own, but I can't wait to get out there," he said. "This whole experience has been a dream."

Enterpris
0870 350 3000
www.enterpris
MULTI STAR

Are You A Genuine Fan?

Starting in the blue box at the top of page 49, answer the questions, go with the flow, and find out whether you are Shayne's biggest fan – or only vaguely aware of the man. You can follow only a pink arrow into a question box and a blue arrow out of it.

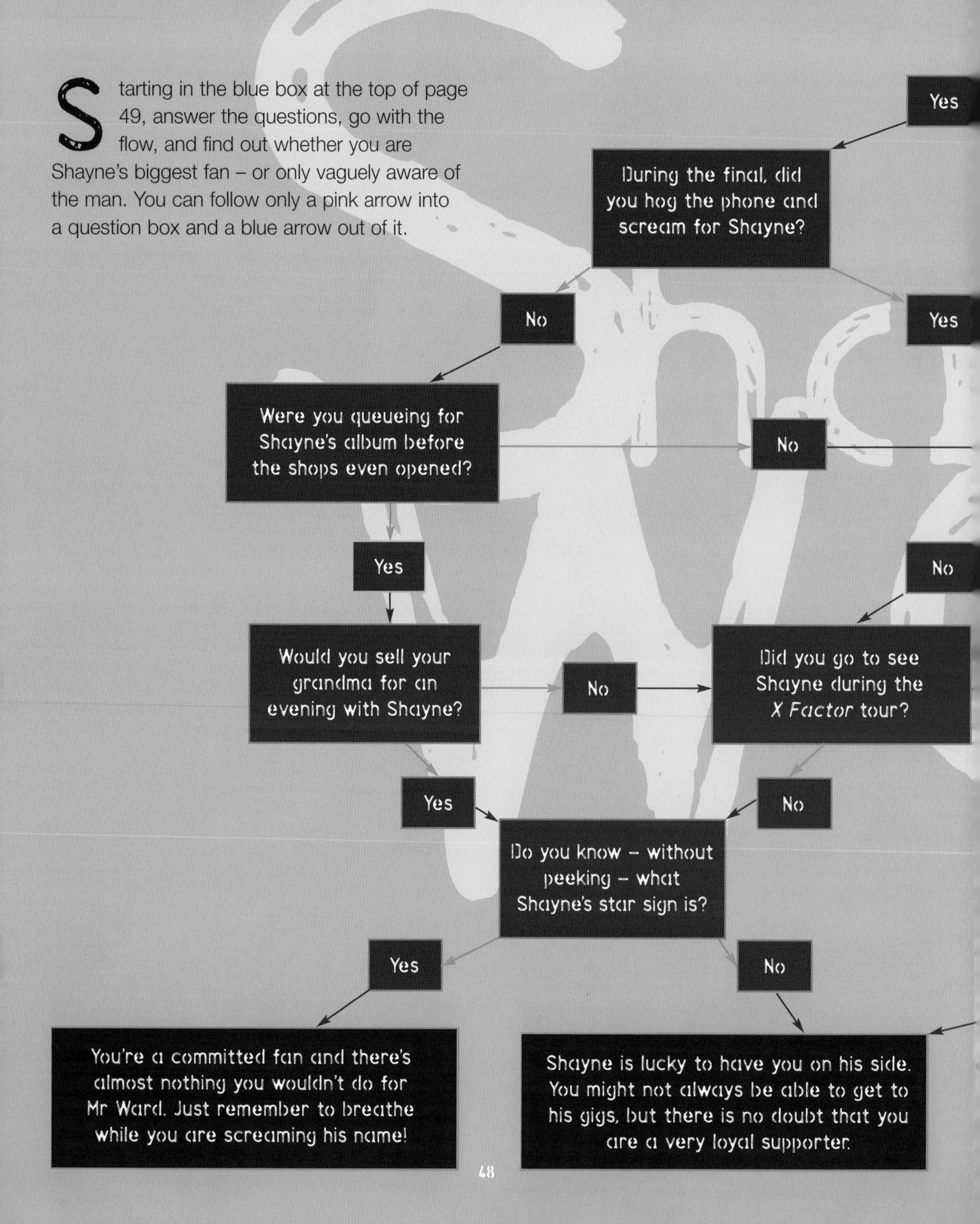

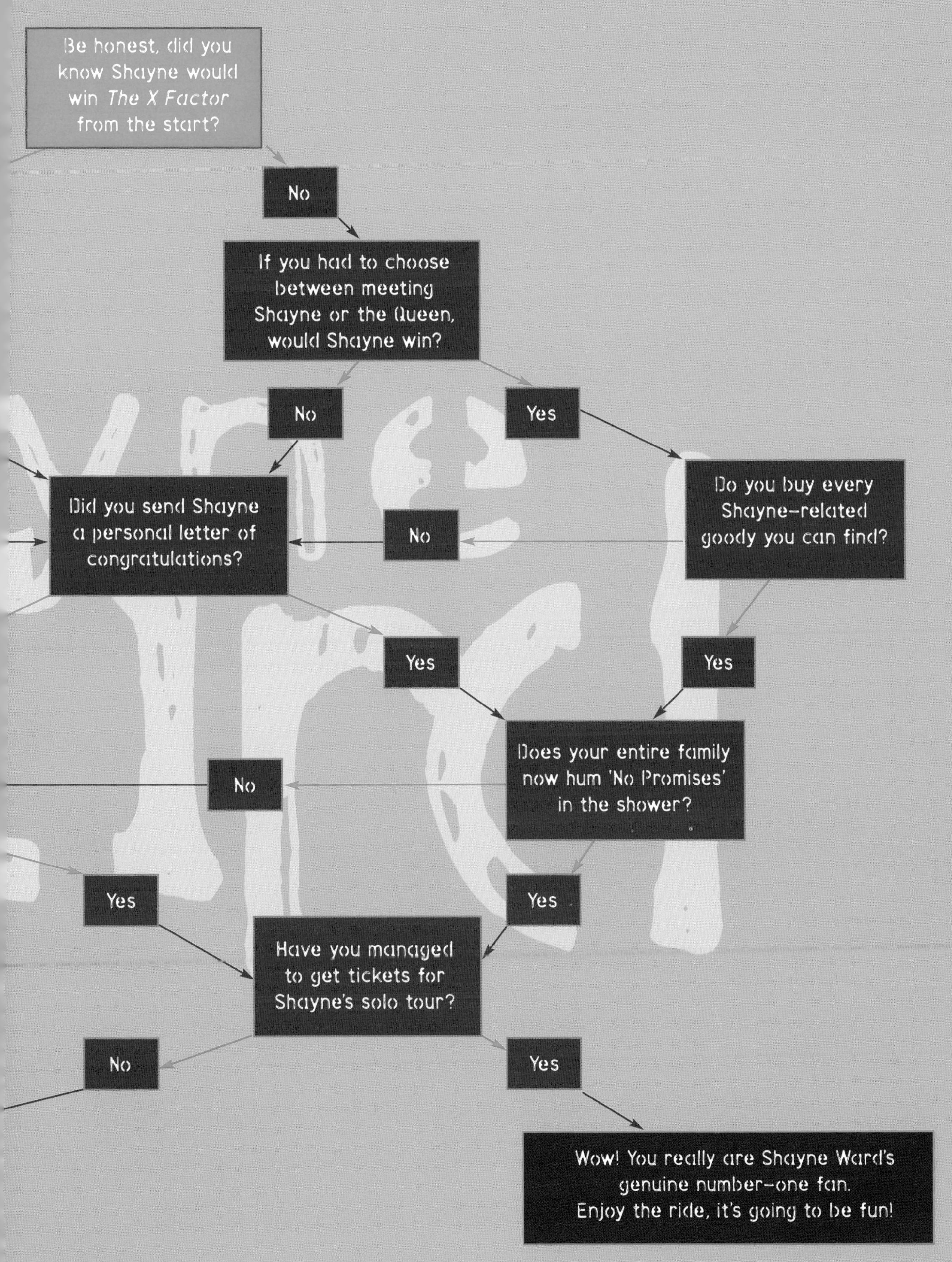
Be honest, did you know Shayne would win The X Factor from the start?
No
If you had to choose between meeting Shayne or the Queen, would Shayne win?
No
Yes
Do you buy every Shayne-related goody you can find?
No
Did you send Shayne a personal letter of congratulations?
Yes
Yes
Does your entire family now hum 'No Promises' in the shower?
No
Yes
Yes
Have you managed to get tickets for Shayne's solo tour?
No
Yes
Wow! You really are Shayne Ward's genuine number-one fan. Enjoy the ride, it's going to be fun!

Shayne Splashes The Cash

Along with the celebrity friends, the screaming fans and the non-stop musical achievements, Shayne has had to get used to something else – money! With a million-pound contract and lucrative advertising deals, Shayne is doing very well for himself.

It's a far cry from his previous life, when his earnings peaked just above the minimum wage. "I can't remember exactly what it was, but it was definitely less than £500 a month, take home," he admits.

Even before *The X Factor* finished, Shayne had decided what he would spend the money on if he won. "The first thing I'd buy would be a new house for my mum," he said. And sure enough, forget the flowers and the chocolates, Shayne's mum received a house on Mother's Day, 2006. It was the first serious money spent by her celebrity son. "She is brilliant and really deserves it," he says. "She saw the house a while ago, but I told her the deal had fallen through. She was so excited when I told her I was only joking! I hope when I go back to visit there will always be a room for me – or a couch!" We're sure there will be.

And what about Shayne shopping for Shayne? Here are some of the things he has spent his money on:

- A penthouse suite in a plush new development – sadly, he hasn't had the chance to move in yet.
- A widescreen, top-of-the-range plasma TV set – perfect for watching his latest TV appearances on.
- Bottles of *Bvlgari BLVG* – his favourite aftershave.
- Clothes – Shayne has splashed out on some super-trendy threads over the past few months, with funky jeans and trousers, some very sexy vest tops, wide-collared shirts and designer suits for those celebrity parties.
- A black Gucci suit – the suit was specially designed for Shayne and David Beckham alone – and some flashy diamond earrings, just like Beckham's!

Manchester United Rocks

Music is obviously Shayne's number-one obsession, but football is important, too. There is only one club for our favourite Mancunian pop star – Manchester United, of course.

Since he was brought up in the city, it is not surprising that Shayne supports Manchester's premier-league club. He is potty about it! "I'd love to have been a footballer for Manchester United. I'm a good player, actually. I never went for trials, though," he says. It's probably a good job – we'd much rather see him on stage!

If Shayne could buy a player for his team, he knows who he'd go for. "Ronaldinho. He is amazing. They've got to challenge Chelsea next season," he warns.

Thanks to his new celebrity status and the associated earnings, Shayne can now get closer to his favourite football stars than ever before – quite literally. The plush new home he has plumped for will see him become neighbour to Manchester United players Ryan Giggs and Gary Neville.

But it's not just Manchester United that gets Shayne's vote – the England team has his full backing. "I love to watch England play," he admits. "It can be difficult to find the time, but I'm pretty determined."

Shayne

Celebrity Pals

Shayne's loyalty to his old friends is legendary – there's no doubt that they will always have a special place in his heart. But fellow celebrities are keen to get to know our pop idol – well, who wouldn't be?

Robbie Williams

One of Shayne's best-known new pals is Robbie Williams, who thinks Shayne is very much like him. Shortly after *The X Factor* finished, Robbie said he thought Shayne was "the next Robbie". "He said loads of people had come up to him saying I was following in his footsteps. I'm not sure if that is right or not. I reckon it depends on what direction I take – whether the record company lets me be cheeky!" Shayne comments.

Football Friends

Shayne was chosen to take part in a Soccer Aid tournament, joining teammates Robbie Williams, Jude Law and Orlando Bloom to play against celebrity chef Gordon Ramsay's team for charity. We'd certainly have liked to have been on the touchline for that game!

Daniel Bedingfield

When it comes to the music side of things, Daniel Bedingfield gets Shayne's vote. Daniel's hit song 'If You're Not The One', which helped Shayne on his road to stardom, is a clear favourite and Shayne would love to do a duet with Daniel. In fact, he has already met Daniel at a party, but ended up getting punched on the arm. "I think he was being friendly, though," Shayne says. We're sure he was ...

Leonardo DiCaprio

It isn't only singers who have succumbed to the charms of the Mancunian crooner – Shayne met Leo DiCaprio and toasted in the New Year with him at a party on the beaches of Miami. A host of Hollywood celebrities, including Renée Zellweger and Bruce Willis, partied with them. Afterwards, Shayne said, "I'm just somewhere up in the clouds right now. I've met so many amazing people."

Feet On The Ground

Despite having met so many serious A-listers, Shayne is not going to go crazy. "I'm so serious about my music," he declares. "You'll never see me falling out of a club. I promise," he says. And Shayne remains true to the people who helped him at the beginning of his career. Of *The X Factor* judges, Shayne says, "In my eyes, the biggest stars I've met are the three judges – Sharon, Simon and Louis." We're sure they love you too, Shayne.

Shayne Ward

Quick Quiz

Now you can test the knowledge of your favourite pop idol you'll have picked up from reading this book. The answers are below, so when you have finished, count up your correct answers and find out what your score says about you.

1. What did Shayne buy his mum after winning *The X Factor*?
2. Which song, originally by Queen, helped Shayne to fame?
3. Who was Shayne's mentor on *The X Factor*'s panel of judges?
4. Where was Shayne born?
5. Which designer made a suit specially for Shayne and David Beckham?
6. Who would Shayne like to play him in a film of his life?
7. With which A-list celebrities did Shayne toast in the New Year?
8. Who would Shayne most like to do a duet with?
9. How many girlfriends did Shayne have at school?
10. What was Shayne's second chart single called?

Answers

1. A house
2. 'Don't Stop Me Now'
3. Louis Walsh
4. Hattersley, Tameside, Greater Manchester
5. Gucci
6. Justin Timberlake
7. Leonardo DiCaprio, Bruce Willis and Renée Zellweger
8. Daniel Bedingfield
9. Two
10. 'No Promises'

Ward-search Answers (page 31)

What Your Score Means

0 – 3

Go back to the Shayne Ward School! You must have been asleep for the past year. It's time to wake up and catch up on all the action.

4 – 7

You've been following Shayne's progress, but you're not quite his number-one fan yet. If you want to impress our boy, you might want to swot up on all of the lovely things that make him tick.

8 – 10

You are simply a top fan! You've been watching Shayne on screen since day one, and you'll quite happily spend all of your spare cash on Shayne's singles and on any magazines featuring our hunky star. You haven't missed a beat yet, and there's no way you're going to. He'd be chuffed to bits.

CASINO
bowling
wood bowl

The Future's Bright

Shayne's success has been staggering and we feel sure his fame will continue to grow. Here are a few highlights to look forward to in the coming year, plus some of Shayne's own advice to wannabe pop idols.

Arena Tour

It looks like it's going to be another busy year for Shayne. Our favourite lad will kick off his solo tour in February, and fans across the UK and Ireland will be treated to some live action.

Songwriting

Songwriting could also be on the cards for the singer. Shayne is keen to try his hand at penning his own tunes, and we're fairly sure the soulful crooner has some hits in him. Meanwhile, we're pretty happy with the songs he has been performing so far!

Experimentation

Pop has been the word so far from Shayne, but jazz, blues, folk ... there's no limit to what Shayne could turn his versatile voice to next. He's not ruling anything out. Shayne is willing to experiment to achieve more hits. "It depends what suits my voice best, really," he says. And if the past year is anything to go on, we're sure there will be more chart-topping action from Shayne. After all, mentor Louis is looking to make him the next Will Young.

Go For It

For all of you at home with a passion for music and dream of stardom, Shayne's advice is to stop doubting yourself and go for it. "You could end up here like I am today," he says. "Don't let anyone put you down." Shayne's future is bright maybe yours is too.